Maximus
and the television

© 1996 Scripture Union
Text copyright © 1996 Brian Ogden
Illustrations copyright © 1996 Elke Counsell
First published 1996.

Scripture Union, 207–209 Queensway,
Bletchley, Milton Keynes MK2 2EB, England.

ISBN 1 85999 055 X

Designed by Tony Cantale Graphics.

Printed in Singapore by Tien Wah Press.

Maximus
and the television

Brian Ogden

Illustrated by Elke Counsell

Scripture Union

'Are you coming out, Maximus? There's a Mammoth Cheese Sale at Squeaker's Supermarket today,' asked Paula.

'Sorry, but it's all my favourite cartoons on TV this afternoon – I always watch *Tom and Jerry*. Jerry's my hero. Then there's *Mouse Party* and then there's *Next Door Mice*, all about the mice in Australia. Can't possibly come out today.'

Patrick and Paula went off to do their shopping, leaving Maximus propped up against the wall, eyes glued to the television.

'I don't know what we can do about Maximus,' said Patrick. 'He's worse than the children at sitting and watching TV all the time. He used to come and play footsnail or go for a long scamper over the graveyard. Now, all he does is sit and watch the box.'

'I know what you mean,' replied his wife. 'Let's see if he will come to supper this evening – you know how he likes his food. Perhaps that will get him away for a while.'

Later that evening, Patrick popped round to the vestry whilst Paula cooked a lovely meal of roast hymn book. He found Maximus in the same place as he had left him, in front of the TV.

'Sh ... quiet a moment,' said Maximus, holding a paw to his lips. 'Just want to see what happens.'

Patrick waited until the programme had finished and the advertisements started. There was one about two mice drinking a special coffee and another one with a lady mouse holding up a clean shirt, saying, 'I'll always use Percy Washing Powder – I won't swap a packet of Percy for two packets of my old powder, or for anything!'

'Maximus, Paula has sent me round to ask you to –'

'Sh ... that's my favourite ad and now I've missed it,' said Maximus. 'What do you want?'

'Maximus! Please listen for a moment. We want you to come to supper,' Patrick shouted above the noise of the TV.

'Couldn't possibly – thanks all the same. There's a special film about Blue Max – the great flying mouse. He was my great, great, great, great, great, great uncle. At least, I think that's enough greats – could be two more. Anyway, he was really famous and my mum and dad named me after him. Max, that is – not Blue.'

Patrick gave up and went back to Paula.

'I'm sorry, love, but I can't shift him away from the TV. He just seems to watch it all the time. He's not eating properly, he's not getting any fresh air, in fact he will make himself really ill soon. We've got to do something.'

'Well, stop worrying now. If Maximus isn't coming, then there's more food for us and the children. I think I might have a plan. I'll tell you after supper.'

At the end of the meal, Paula told Patrick what her plan was. Patrick just laughed and laughed. It was brilliant.

Next morning, Maximus had to go shopping. There were no more TV meals in the fridge, no more cornflakes in the packet, and what was most important, no food to be found by scampering around the church. It was the shops or starve.

This was the moment Patrick and Paula had been waiting for. When they were quite sure that Maximus had left the church, they hid Maximus' TV behind a curtain and dragged a large box into the vestry. They cut a square opening in the front and glued two small knobs on the side. They set the box where the TV had been and Patrick then crept out, leaving Paula behind the box.

A few moments later Maximus returned, carrying a large plastic bag full of packets of worm-flavoured crisps, cans of Mousade and a Mouse Pride loaf of bread. He settled himself down near the box and, without looking very closely, just turned one of the knobs.

Paula moved to the opening in the front of the box and began to speak: 'Welcome, viewers, to our new programme on health. Today, I am going to squeak about the dangers of television. It is a sad fact that many of you watching me will already be suffering from that dreadful disease, telisitis. Slowly, as you watch more and more television, the disease gets a hold of you. Your eyes begin to develop lines across them and the skin round the edge forms a rectangular shape. You begin to lose the use of your legs due to sitting too long. You only eat ready-made meals – I can see some of you, now, dipping your paws into another packet of crisps.'

At this, Maximus dropped the bag of crisps and started to listen even harder. Paula had great difficulty keeping a straight face and her whiskers began to twitch. She went on: 'I have come, this morning, to warn you that if you suffer from any of these symptoms then you must do three things. Firstly, you must turn off the set. Secondly, you must go outside, so your eyes get used to daylight. Thirdly, you must go for a long walk so that your legs are stretched and used.

'Now, on the count of three, follow those rules – TV off, go out and exercise. ONE, TWO, THREE.'

Maximus slowly stood up. He walked to the box
and turned the knob without looking at it and went out
of the vestry. By the time Patrick had crept in, Paula
was laughing so hard that tears were running down her
cheeks.

That evening, Maximus knocked on the Sunday School cupboard door.

'Er ... I don't suppose I could come to supper tonight?' he asked.

'Of course, Maximus,' said Paula. 'You know you're always welcome.'

'Nothing interesting on the TV tonight?' asked Patrick, nudging Paula under the table.

'No,' said Maximus. 'I choose carefully what I watch. It can get a hold on you if you're not careful! I prefer to get out in the fresh air!'

Heavenly Father,
Thank you for all the pleasure that television gives,
for what we can learn of your world and the way we can
know what is happening to our neighbours all over the world.
Help us to use it wisely and not to be tempted to sit
and watch when other things are more important.
Amen.